MAKING THE GRADE

EASY POPULAR PIECES FOR YOUNG VIOLINISTS. SELECTED AND ARRAN

Published by
Chester Music
8/9 Frith Street, London W1D 3JB, England.

Exclusive Distributors:
Music Sales Limited
Distribution Centre, Newmarket Road, Bury St. Edmunds, Suffolk IP33 3YB, England.
Music Sales Pty Limited
120 Rothschild Avenue, Rosebery, NSW 2018, Australia.

Music arranged and processed by Jerry Lanning.
Edited by Heather Ramage.
Printed in the United Kingdom by Caligraving Limited, Thetford, Norfolk.

CD recorded, mixed and mastered by Jonas Persson.
Violin by Dermot Crehan

www.musicsales.com

Chester Music
part of The Music Sales Group
London/New York/Paris/Sydney/Copenhagen/Berlin/Madrid/Tokyo

INTRODUCTION

This collection of 21 popular tunes has been carefully arranged and graded to provide attractive teaching repertoire for young violinists. The familiarity of the material will stimulate pupils' enthusiasm and encourage their practice.

The technical demands of the solo part increase progressively up to the standard of Associated Board Grade 1. The piano accompaniments are simple yet effective and should be within the range of most pianists.

Practical suggestions for bowing are given, but these may of course be adapted to suit the needs of the individual student. It is important always to feel a steady pulse, so that bow speeds can be planned appropriately.

ANY DREAM WILL DO

(from "Joseph and the Amazing Technicolor® Dreamcoat")

Music by Andrew Lloyd Webber. Lyrics by Tim Rice

Take care with the dotted rhythms. Keep the semiquavers light and try to match the accompaniment.

THE SKATER'S WALTZ

By Emil Waldteufel

Make your bow changes as smooth as possible.

EENSY, WEENSY SPIDER

American traditional

The tempo should be quick enough to feel two beats in a bar.

PAVANE

(from "The Capriol Suite")

By Peter Warlock

Try for a smooth, sustained sound, and be aware of the four bar phrases.

I'M POPEYE THE SAILOR MAN

Words & Music by Sammy Lerner

This piece needs a bright and breezy performance!

EDELWEISS

(from "The Sound of Music")

Words by Oscar Hammerstein II. Music by Richard Rodgers

Play each phrase as smoothly as possible. Listen carefully to the tuning.

O NO, JOHN!

English traditional

Play the last four bars quite forcefully, for contrast.

SARABANDE

(from "Keyboard Suite IX")

By George Frideric Handel

Pay careful attention to the rests in this piece.

Very slow and stately

I HAVE A DREAM

Words & Music by Benny Andersson & Björn Ulvaeus

Be sure to hold the long notes for their full length.

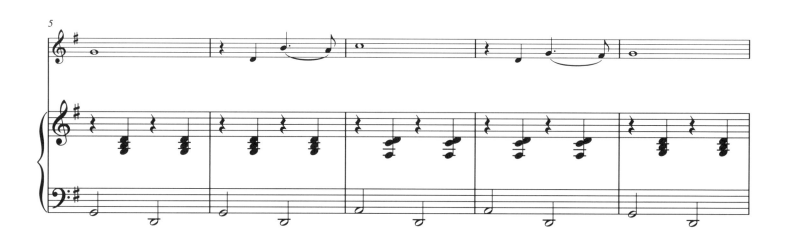

13

THE YELLOW ROSE OF TEXAS

American traditional

Play with a full sound, and try not to drag.

JEAN DE FLORETTE (THEME)

By Jean-Claude Petit

Although this is a gentle piece, use enough bow to develop a good sound.

15

NO MATTER WHAT

Music by Andrew Lloyd Webber. Words by Jim Steinman

Take care with the start of each phrase. It's very easy to be late!

MAKING THE GRADE · GRADE 1

EASY POPULAR PIECES FOR YOUNG VIOLINISTS. SELECTED AND ARRANGED BY JERRY LANNING

VIOLIN PART

Chester Music
part of The Music Sales Group
London/New York/Paris/Sydney/Copenhagen/Berlin/Madrid/Tokyo

Published by
Chester Music
8/9 Frith Street, London W1D 3JB, England.

Exclusive Distributors:
Music Sales Limited
Distribution Centre, Newmarket Road, Bury St. Edmunds, Suffolk IP33 3YB, England.
Music Sales Pty Limited
120 Rothschild Avenue, Rosebery, NSW 2018, Australia.

Order No. CH67397-01
This book © Copyright 2003 by Chester Music.

Music arranged and processed by Jerry Lanning.
Edited by Heather Ramage.
Printed in the United Kingdom by Caligraving Limited, Thetford, Norfolk.

www.musicsales.com

ANY DREAM WILL DO

(from "Joseph and the Amazing Technicolor® Dreamcoat")

Music by Andrew Lloyd Webber. Lyrics by Tim Rice

Take care with the dotted rhythms. Keep the semiquavers light and try to match the accompaniment.

THE SKATER'S WALTZ

By Emil Waldteufel

Make your bow changes as smooth as possible.

EENSY, WEENSY SPIDER

American traditional

The tempo should be quick enough to feel two beats in a bar.

Quite lively

PAVANE

(from "The Capriol Suite")

By Peter Warlock

Try for a smooth, sustained sound, and be aware of the four bar phrases.

Very steady

4

I'M POPEYE THE SAILOR MAN

Words & Music by Sammy Lerner

This piece needs a bright and breezy performance!

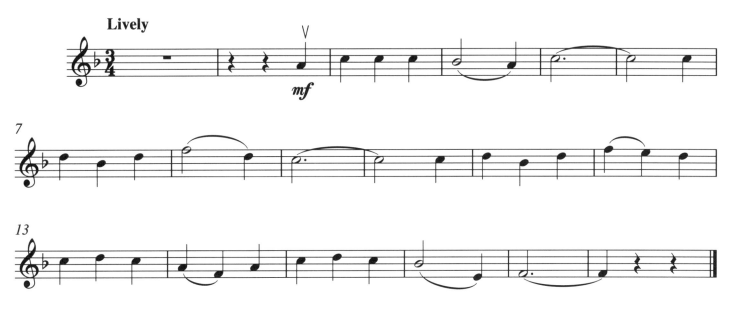

EDELWEISS

(from "The Sound of Music")

Words by Oscar Hammerstein II. Music by Richard Rodgers

Play each phrase as smoothly as possible. Listen carefully to the tuning.

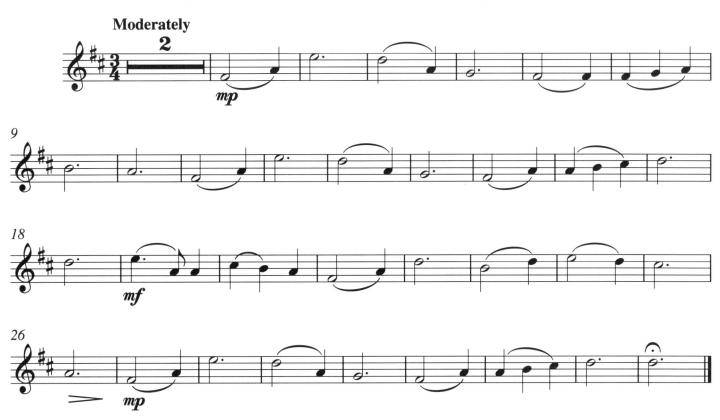

O NO, JOHN!

English traditional

Play the last four bars quite forcefully, for contrast.

Brightly

SARABANDE

(from "Keyboard Suite IX")

By George Frideric Handel

Pay careful attention to the rests in this piece.

Very slow and stately

I HAVE A DREAM

Words & Music by Benny Andersson & Björn Ulvaeus

Be sure to hold the long notes for their full length.

THE YELLOW ROSE OF TEXAS

American traditional

Play with a full sound, and try not to drag.

JEAN DE FLORETTE (THEME)

By Jean-Claude Petit

Although this is a gentle piece, use enough bow to develop a good sound.

NO MATTER WHAT

Music by Andrew Lloyd Webber. Words by Jim Steinman

Take care with the start of each phrase. It's very easy to be late!

HEY HEY ARE YOU READY TO PLAY
(Tweenies Theme)

Music by Graham Pike & Liz Kitchen. Words by Will Brenton & Ian Lauchlan

Listen hard to the tuning of the octave leaps. Keep the rhythm relaxed.

GUANTANAMERA

Music adaptation by Pete Seeger & Julian Orbon. Words adapted by Julian Orbon from a poem by José Marti

Keep the rhythm very steady. When a phrase ends with a quaver, play the quaver lightly.

10

BARBIE GIRL

Words & Music by Soren Rasted, Claus Norreen, Rene Dif,
Lene Nystrom, Johnny Pederson & Karsten Delgado

Take care not to hold on to the quaver at the end of bar four.

THE PHANTOM OF THE OPERA

(from "The Phantom of the Opera")

Music by Andrew Lloyd Webber. Lyrics by Charles Hart. Additional Lyrics by Richard Stilgoe & Mike Batt.

Be absolutely precise with the dotted crotchet/quaver rhythms.

LAND OF HOPE AND GLORY

By Edward Elgar

Try for a very smooth, sustained sound. Don't let the tempo drag.

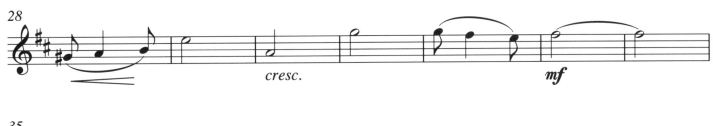

ALL MY LOVING

Words & Music by John Lennon & Paul McCartney

Be careful to read the rhythms carefully – don't guess!

SOMETHIN' STUPID

Words & Music by C. Carson Parks

Articulate the repeated quavers neatly and evenly.

OOM PAH PAH

(from "Oliver")

Words & Music by Lionel Bart

This piece needs a strong performance, but the middle section should be softer and smoother for contrast.

14

DANCE TO YOUR DADDY

English traditional

Accent the first beat of each bar slightly, but play the other notes quite lightly.

5/04 (51367)

HEY HEY ARE YOU READY TO PLAY

(Tweenies Theme)

Music by Graham Pike & Liz Kitchen. Words by Will Brenton & Ian Lauchlan

Listen hard to the tuning of the octave leaps. Keep the rhythm relaxed.

Steady swing

GUANTANAMERA

Music adaptation by Pete Seeger & Julian Orbon. Words adapted by Julian Orbon from a poem by José Marti

Keep the rhythm very steady. When a phrase ends with a quaver, play the quaver lightly.

BARBIE GIRL

Words & Music by Soren Rasted, Claus Norreen, Rene Dif,
Lene Nystrom, Johnny Pederson & Karsten Delgado

Take care not to hold on to the quaver at the end of bar four.

THE PHANTOM OF THE OPERA

(from "The Phantom of the Opera")

Music by Andrew Lloyd Webber. Lyrics by Charles Hart. Additional Lyrics by Richard Stilgoe & Mike Batt.

Be absolutely precise with the dotted crotchet/quaver rhythms.

LAND OF HOPE AND GLORY

By Edward Elgar

Try for a very smooth, sustained sound. Don't let the tempo drag.

ALL MY LOVING

Words & Music by John Lennon & Paul McCartney

Be careful to read the rhythms carefully – don't guess!

27

SOMETHIN' STUPID

Words & Music by C. Carson Parks

Articulate the repeated quavers neatly and evenly.

OOM PAH PAH

(from "Oliver")

Words & Music by Lionel Bart

This piece needs a strong performance, but the middle section should be softer and smoother for contrast.

DANCE TO YOUR DADDY

English traditional

Accent the first beat of each bar slightly, but play the other notes quite lightly.

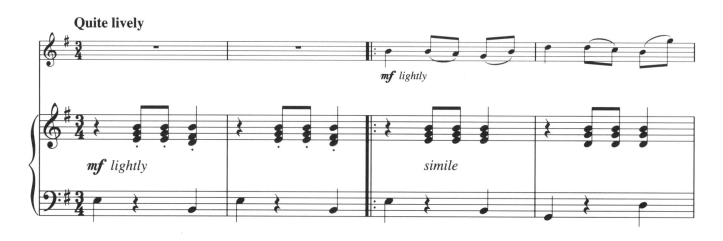

5/04 (51367)